This book belongs to

____

Written by Susan Hood
Illustrated by Joe Ewers

Published by Dalmatian Press, LLC, 2013. All rights reserved.
Franklin, Tennessee 37067. No part of this book may be reproduced or copied in any form without written permission from the copyright owner. 1-866-418-2572

Printed in China

"Elmo," said Bert, "will you help me watch the Fix-It Shop for Luis and Maria?"

Elmo had been looking for a little lost black puppy, but he thought it would be fun to be the manager for a day.

"Let's open for business," said Bert.
"Here's someone now!" Elmo exclaimed. "Hello, Herry! What's wrong?"

"I need Maria and Luis to take care of my toy monster right away," said Herry.

"We'll ask them when they come back tomorrow," said Bert.

"Tomorrow?" cried Herry. "I wanted my monster tonight! I cannot sleep without him. Please, can't you help?"

Elmo watched Herry trudge sadly away.

"We have to fix his doll, Bert!" Elmo said.

So Bert and Elmo got busy. Bert pulled all the leaves out of the doll's fur. But Herry's doll was not fixed.

Elmo took all the burrs out of the doll's fur. But Herry's doll was not fixed.

After lunch, more friends were waiting outside the shop. Ernie came in with his broken wagon.

"Hey, Bert. I need to buy a new wheel," he said.

Snuffy came in carrying a chair with broken legs.
"Uncle Phineus sat on it," he explained.
"I will need a tool for that," said Bert.

When the last monster in line was gone, Bert and Elmo went back to Herry's doll. They stitched some rips and gave him a bubble bath.

They combed out the doll's tangles. Then they put him in the window where anyone walking by the building could see him.

"You fixed him!" shouted Herry Monster when he saw his doll. "You fixed my darling Teddy monster! Oh, thank you!"

Elmo and Bert beamed. "We fixed him all by ourselves!" they said with pride.

After the last customer had left, Bert and Elmo locked the door and headed home. As they walked through the neighborhood, Elmo told Bert about the little lost puppy.

"Don't worry, Elmo," said Bert. "I bet that puppy found a nice place to take a nap."

And Bert was right. He had.

LOST PUPPY
ARUI SE HABLA
CLOSED

Elmo's Everyday Words

busy

Very active. People can be busy working or playing. A place is busy when it's filled with people.
When are you busy?

buy

To get something in exchange for money.
Name something that doesn't cost a thing.

customer

Someone who buys something or asks for help in a shop.
How do you ask for help to find what you need?

line

A group of people standing in a row. It also means a long, thin mark. Line can mean lots of things! Where do you see lines?

manager

The person in charge of a store, business, or team. A manager helps everyone do a good job.
How do you say "nice work"?

open

Not shut or closed; people or things can go in and out.
How can you tell when a shop is open for business?

please

A polite way to ask for something you want.
Please always try to ask for something politely.
When do you say "please"?

shop

A place where things are sold, made, or fixed.
When you go shopping, you visit stores to buy
things you need. What do you shop for?

thank you

A way to say you feel grateful to someone.
Talk about the last time you said "thank you."

tomorrow

The day that comes after today. A night
needs to pass before tomorrow arrives.
What will happen tomorrow?

tool

A machine or other thing people use to do their
work. Hammers and screwdrivers are tools used to
fix things. Name some tools your family has at home.

Big Bird's BIG Ideas

building

A place with a roof, walls, floors, and ceilings: like a house, for example. It also means putting something together.
What is your building like?

fix

To repair something that's broken or hurt. You can also fix things you can't see. If you hurt a person's feelings, saying "I'm sorry" helps.
What else can be fixed?

pride

The good feeling you have about yourself or something you've done. You can also feel pride in the achievements of other people.
What makes you feel pride?

neighborhood

The people and places that are near your home. Some neighborhoods have shops to supply the people with things they want and help they need.
Are there shops in your neighborhood?

Do You See What I See?

What words would YOU use to talk about these things that might be in shops near your home? Think of as many different words as you can. Share your words with a friend!